Little
Sticker Dolly Dressing
Ballerinas

Written by Fiona Watt
Illustrated by Lizzie Mackay
Designed by Antonia Miller

Contents

2 Bella the ballerina

4 Swan Lake

6 The Firebird

8 The Nutcracker

10 The Sleeping Beauty

12 Aurora's wedding

14 Coppélia

15 Petrushka

16 Waltz of the snowflakes

18 The clog dance

20 Cinderella

22 The seasons

24 Curtain call

Sticker pages

The back cover folds out so you can "park" spare
stickers while you dress the ballerinas.

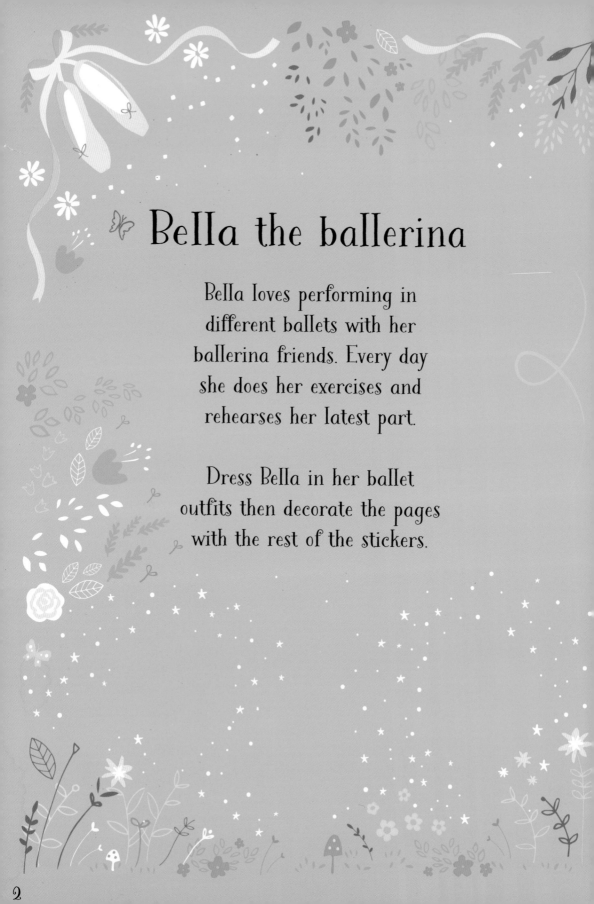

Bella the ballerina

Bella loves performing in
different ballets with her
ballerina friends. Every day
she does her exercises and
rehearses her latest part.

Dress Bella in her ballet
outfits then decorate the pages
with the rest of the stickers.

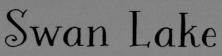

Swan Lake

Bella and her friend Freya are performing in Swan Lake. Bella is one of the little swans and Freya is Odette, the beautiful princess who has been turned into a swan by an evil magician.

The Firebird

At night, the firebird flies into a King's enchanted garden and steals a golden apple from a magical tree. A handsome prince catches her and refuses to release her. She offers him one of her feathers and tells him it will help him if he is ever in trouble.

The Nutcracker

Clara's godfather gives her a nutcracker doll at her family's Christmas party. The doll magically tranforms into a handsome prince who whisks Clara away to the Land of Sweets, home of the Sugar Plum Fairy.

The Sleeping Beauty

Bella is dancing the role of Princess Aurora, in
The Sleeping Beauty, who had a spell cast on her by a
wicked fairy. She pricks her finger at her sixteenth birthday
party, but instead of dying she falls into a deep sleep.

With the Lilac Fairy's help,
handsome Prince Florimund wakes
Aurora with a kiss. They fall in love
and he asks her to marry him.

Aurora's Wedding

From The Sleeping Beauty

Fairytale characters, including a blue bird
and a white cat, are guests at the grand party
being held in celebration of Princess Aurora
and Prince Florimund's wedding.

Coppélia

Every morning a beautiful young girl sits on
a balcony reading a book. Townsfolk try
and attract her attention, but she ignores them
because she's actually a mechanical doll.

Petrushka

Sophia is dancing the part of a puppet
in the ballet, Petrushka. When a magician
puts on a puppet show, the puppets come
alive to the sound of his magical flute.

Waltz of the snowflakes

From The Nutcracker

Welcome to the Land of Snow,
where snowflake ballerinas pirouette and jump
as if they're being blown around by an icy wind.

The clog dance

From La Fille mal gardée

It's the end of harvest time and the farm workers are celebrating by dancing in the fields. Some of them are even dancing in their heavy wooden clogs.

Bella and some of the other ballerinas are dressed as farm workers. They will perform a lively folk dance around a maypole.

Cinderella

Cinderella is alone in the house while her father
and stepsisters attend a royal ball. A beggar
knocks on the door asking for food. Cinderella
gives her some bread and the beggar leaves.

Suddenly the beggar reappears, transformed
into a Fairy Godmother. With a wave
of her wand she tells Cinderella
that she too can go to the ball.

The Seasons

From Cinderella

Bella's friends Natalie and Maddie are dancing
the part of the Spring and Summer fairies
who change Cinderella's ragged clothes into a
beautiful gown suitable for the royal ball.

Curtain call

The performance is over. Bella walks to the front of the stage as the curtains swoosh open. As she curtseys the audience cheers and applauds loudly.

First published in 2016 by Usborne Publishing Ltd., Usborne House, 83-85 Saffron Hill, London, EC1N 8RT, England. www.usborne.com Copyright © 2016 Usborne Publishing Ltd. The name Usborne and the devices 🎈🎈 are Trade Marks of Usborne Publishing Ltd. All rights reserved. No part of this publication may be reproduced, stored in a retrieval system, or transmitted in any form or by any means, electronic, mechanical, photocopying, recording or otherwise without the prior permission of the publisher. First published in America 2016. UE

Bella the ballerina
Pages 2-3

Put the top on
before the skirt.

Put Bella's top on before her skirt.

Freya's outfit

The Firebird
Pages 6-7

The Firebird's headdress

Put the skirt on before the top.

The Firebird is holding this apple.

The Nutcracker
Pages 8-9

Put the top on first.

Put the top on first.

Put the Sugar Plum Fairy's top on before her skirt.

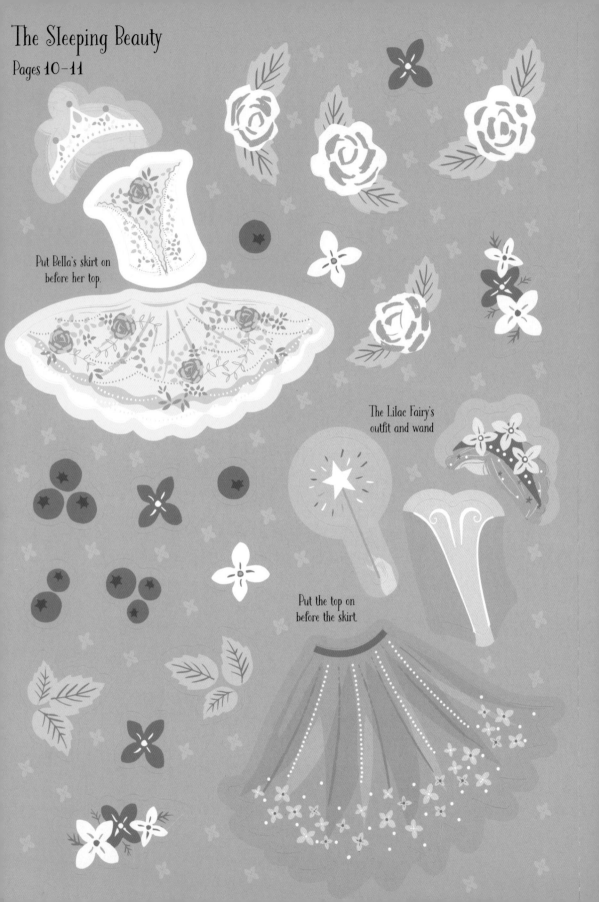

The Sleeping Beauty

Put Bella's skirt on before her top.

The Lilac Fairy's outfit and wand

Put the top on before the skirt

Aurora's Wedding
Pages 12-13

Put the Bluebird's top on before the skirt.

Put the White Cat's top on first.

Petrushka
Page 15

Coppélia
Page 14

Coppélia's top should go on before her skirt.

Put Petruska's skirt on first.

Waltz of the snowflakes
Pages 16–17

Put the top on first.

Put the skirt on first.

The clog dance
Pages 18-19

Put the top
on first.

Put Bella's top on
before her skirt.

Cinderella
Pages 20-21

Put Cinderella's top on before her skirt.

Put the Fairy Godmother's skirt on before her top.

The Seasons
Page 22

Spring's headdress
and skirt

Summer
Page 23

Put Summer's
top on first

Curtain call
Page 24

Bella's skirt